James and the Kindergartener

The Lion and the Mouse Remixed

BY CONNIE COLWELL MILLER   ILLUSTRATED BY VICTORIA ASSANELLI

AMICUS ILLUSTRATED is published by Amicus
P.O. Box 1329, Mankato, MN 56002
www.amicuspublishing.us

*For Miles, who reads more books about dragons than any boy
I know.* —C.C.M.

LIBRARY OF CONGRESS CATALOGING-IN-PUBLICATION DATA
Names: Miller, Connie Colwell, 1976- author. | Assanelli, Victoria, 1984– illustrator. | Aesop.
Title: James and the kindergartener : the lion and the mouse remixed / by Connie Colwell Miller ;
illustrated by Victoria Assanelli.
Other titles: Lion and the mouse remixed
Description: Mankato, MN : Amicus Illustrated, [2017] | Series: Aesop's fables remixed |
Summary: "In this modern-day re-telling of Aesop's fable 'The Lion and the Mouse,' James doesn't
turn in a misbehaving kindergartener and in turn, she helps him" — Provided by publisher.
Identifiers: LCCN 2015034232 (print) | LCCN 2015051289 (ebook) | ISBN 9781607539544
(library binding) | ISBN 9781681510781 (ebook) | ISBN 9781681510781 (pdf)
Subjects: | CYAC: Fables. | Folklore.
Classification: LCC PZ8.2.M488 Jam 2017 (print) | LCC PZ8.2.M488 (ebook) |
DDC 398.2 —dc23
LC record available at http://lccn.loc.gov/2015034232

EDITOR: Rebecca Glaser
DESIGNER: Kathleen Petelinsek

Printed in the United States of America at Corporate Graphics in North Mankato, Minnesota.

10 9 8 7 6 5 4 3

ABOUT THE AUTHOR

Connie Colwell Miller is a writer, editor, and instructor who lives in Mankato, Minnesota, with her four children. She has written more than 80 books for young children. She also likes to tell stories to her kids to teach them important life lessons—just like Aesop did in his fables.

ABOUT THE ILLUSTRATOR

Victoria Assanelli was born during the autumn of 1984 in Buenos Aires, Argentina. She spent most of her childhood playing with her grandparents, reading books, and drawing doodles. She began working as an illustrator in 2007, and has illustrated several textbooks and storybooks since.

It was recess time—James's favorite time of day. He loved to sit under the big oak tree and read his dragon books.

Today, the sun was warm. A breeze brushed over him. James held the open book on his lap. He felt himself getting sleepy. Then he nodded off.

When James woke up, his pesky little sister Claire was standing beside him. A group of kids from Claire's kindergarten class stood behind her. James pretended that he was still asleep. What was Claire up to this time?

Claire whispered to her friends, "Watch this!" She pulled a marker from her pocket and poised herself to draw a moustache on James's face.

Before she could make a mark, James grabbed his sister's wrist. "What are you doing. Claire?"

Claire jumped in surprise. "Nothing!" she replied. But James knew better. "You were going to write on me!" he said. "I think I will take you to the principal's office."

Claire's eyes widened. "Please don't tell the principal, James. It was just a joke." James was annoyed. Claire begged. "If you let me go, I will help you one day." James laughed. "How could YOU help ME? You're only a kindergartener!" But James let her go.

After school, James didn't wait for Claire. He usually walked home with his little sister. Today, he was still mad at her. James pulled out his dragon book and read as he walked.

About a block from school, there was a large branch on the sidewalk. James didn't see it.

Ouch! He tripped. His book went flying. He stumbled off the sidewalk and rolled into the bushes.

James couldn't get up, no matter how hard he tried. His backpack was stuck on something. He was just about to yell out for help when he heard small footsteps. He looked up. It was his annoying sister, Claire. She'll probably laugh at me, he thought.

"Claire, will you help me?" James asked. To his surprise, Claire reached into the bush and freed James. "Now where's my book?" James asked. "Here it is!" Claire yelled. She had found it under a low bush. James was too tall to have seen it there.

James didn't feel angry at his sister anymore. He smiled and said, "Thanks, Claire. I guess you were right. Small friends can be a great help."

The Lion and the Mouse

by Aesop

Once upon a time, there was a lion. The lion was taking a nap. A small mouse began to run up and down the lion, annoying him. The lion awoke and grabbed the mouse in his great paw.

The mouse begged the lion. "Please spare my life. One day I will help you." The lion thought this idea was funny. He didn't believe the mouse could ever help him. The mouse was too small!

But one day, hunters caught the lion in a trap. They used ropes to tie him to a tree while they went to get a metal cage. Just then, the little mouse happened by. He gnawed away at the ropes until the lion was free.

The moral of the story is "little friends can be great friends."

Discussion Questions

1. How is James similar to the lion in the fable?

2. How is Claire similar to the mouse?

3. What lesson does James learn from this event?

4. Have you ever behaved like James or Claire?

5. How is the story of James and Claire different from the original fable?

6. How are the two stories similar?

Who Was Aesop?

Many people believe that Aesop was a storyteller from Ancient Greece. He told stories about animal characters that did human things. Aesop's stories were spoken out loud. Later, other people gathered the stories in a collection that is now referred to as "Aesop's Fables." Each of Aesop's fables shares a moral, or important lesson, with the reader.